Find the Frog

t

Look for me hanging around all over the place.

I'm a book worm. Can you find me creeping along?

Wait! Before you go any further...

There's a frog in this book who is trying to hide,
but if you have sharp eyes you will find him inside.

And there's more!

It's not just a frog who is hiding away,
there are others – perhaps you will find them today...

...some pandas, an elephant, penguins in threes,
a hedgehog, a worm and a sloth in the trees?

And you might see a rogue who's committed a crime –
perhaps you can help? Can you catch him in time?

Help me find the robber in every picture. He's good at hiding so it might be tricky.

Dad! Dad! I can see the pandas.
We're supposed to be looking for the frog. Let's get going.

Mum! Mum! I've spotted the penguins already.

Hmmm. Which way to the beginning? It must be just over the page.

Find the Frog

You shouldn't have a problem finding me. I'm big and green and can easily be seen!

Gotta get out of here right now...

Where can that pesky frog be, son? He should be easy to spot.

Stephan Lomp

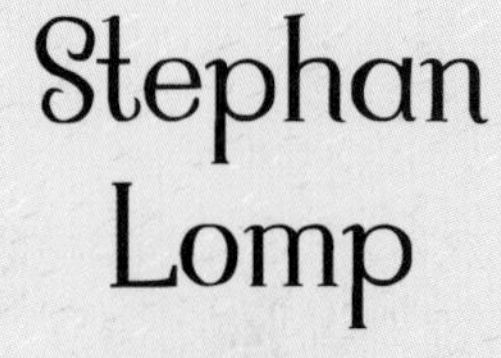

It's light and bright in the park today. Who's singing a song and who's running awa

'ho's rowing a boat and who's out for a jog? Who's having a snooze? And WHERE'S THE FROG?

It’s busy in town. Who’s dropped their fruit? Who’s driving, who’s chasing? Toot toot to

'ho's washing their hair? Who's walking their dog? Who's reading a map? And WHERE'S THE FROG?

The market is bustling. Who's wearing red? Who's wishing for fish and who's getting ahea

Boef
5,-

ɔ's buying a melon fi om Mr Mog? Who's drinking their coffee? And WHERE'S THE FROG?

Now enter the restaurant. Who's slurping their broth? Who's making a mess ar d who's under the clo

ho's squirting sauce on a big hot dog? Who's dropping their dishes? And WHERE'S THE FROG?

Be careful as over the crossing we stride. Who's up on one wheel and who's got a free ric

7 3

ho's jumping a sign and who's lost in the smog? Whose car is the smallest? And WHERE'S THE FROG?

COGS
DRAZIW
7

Now everyone's shopping. Who's got the wrong size? Who's riding the handrail and who's in disguis

ho's munching the news? Who's buying a cog? Who's planning a trip and WHERE'S THE FROG?

Down at the station the trains zoom on by. Who's squeezing on board and who's riding up hig

703
712
713

Who's on the phone and who's tripped on a log? Who's left on their own? And WHERE'S THE FROG?

ZOG

Inside the airport we wait for our jet. Who's driving the luggage? Who's started to swea

ho's hanging around and who's waiting for Zog? Who's stuck on the stairs? And WHERE'S THE FROG?

Into the clear blue sky we go! Who's stealing a drink and who's tucked down belo

ho's in a glider and who's lost a clog? Who's eating a burger? And WHERE'S THE FROG?

73
1
3

Down at the beach, who's building a fort? Who's ready to surf and who's finally caugh

ho's buried in sand and who's feeding their dog? Who's playing a game? And WHERE'S THE FROG?